TITLE :   Tales of Krishna : 3-in-1 /
AUTHOR STAT : editor, Anant Pai.
IMPRINT :   Mumbai India : Amar Chitra Katha Pvt Ltd, April 2017

D.K Agencies (P) Ltd.   DKCHD-5306
www.dkagencies.com

KRISHNA AND RUKMINI

RUKMI, THE SON OF KING BHEESHMAKA OF VIDARBHA, CAME HOME FROM MATHURA, BURSTING WITH NEWS.

AS THE MEMBERS OF THE ROYAL HOUSEHOLD SURROUNDED HIM—

KRISHNA, THE COWHERD FROM VRINDAVAN, HAS SLAIN KAMSA.

1

IT APPEARS THAT KRISHNA IS REALLY THE EIGHTH SON OF VASUDEVA AND DEVAKI, KAMSA'S COUSIN. HE AND HIS ELDER BROTHER, BALARAMA, WERE SECRETED AWAY TO GOKUL AS SOON AS THEY WERE BORN AND WERE BROUGHT UP AMONG THE COWHERDS.

SO IN SPITE OF ALL KAMSA'S EFFORTS THE PROPHECY HAS COME TRUE. IS KRISHNA REALLY A DIVINITY?

RUKMI'S SISTER, RUKMINI, WAS A FORTHRIGHT GIRL.

THEN HE IS NO COWHERD BUT A NOBLE YADAVA!

RUKMINI! HE HAS MURDERED MY FRIEND AND YOU CALL HIM NOBLE.

YOU WILL NEVER ADMIT THAT KAMSA WAS AN EVIL KING. THE YADAVAS OF MATHURA HAD NEVER BEEN HAPPY UNDER HIS RULE. BESIDES...

2

...DON'T FORGET HE DEPOSED HIS OWN FATHER AND USURPED THE THRONE.

I SUPPOSE KRISHNA WILL NOW BECOME THE KING.

NO! HE REFUSED THE CROWN. HE INSISTED THAT UGRASENA BE REINSTATED.

HE REFUSED THE CROWN!

YES! BUT KING UGRASENA AND THE NOBLES HAVE REQUESTED, NAY, INSISTED THAT HE REMAIN IN MATHURA AND...

WHO WOULDN'T! DID HE AGREE?

RUKMI IGNORED HER AND CONTINUED TO SPEAK TO BHEESHMAKA.

HE HAS AGREED TO STAY FOR A WHILE—TO LEARN THE SCRIPTURES AND THE PRINCELY ARTS.

WHAT ABOUT JARASANDHA? HOW DID HE REACT?

3

JARASANDHA, KAMSA'S FATHER-IN-LAW, WAS THE EMPEROR OF MAGADHA, THE MOST POWERFUL KINGDOM OF THOSE DAYS. MATHURA, LIKE VIDARBHA AND MOST OTHER KINGDOMS, OWED ALLEGIANCE TO HIM.

THE EMPEROR IS FURIOUS. BOTH HIS DAUGHTERS* HAVE BEEN WIDOWED IN ONE STROKE. HE VOWS TO TAKE REVENGE. HE HAS SENT FOR ME. I MUST GO AND SEE ABOUT THE CHARIOTS.

RUKMINI FOLLOWED HIM.

I MUST KNOW MORE ABOUT KRISHNA.

BHEESHMAKA AND HIS WIFE WERE ALONE.

THE BOY SEEMS TO BE VIRTUOUS. I CANNOT THINK OF A MORE SUITABLE HUSBAND FOR RUKMINI.

THE SAME THOUGHT OCCURRED TO ME. HE REFUSED THE CROWN OF MATHURA. HOW IT MUST HAVE PLEASED POOR, OLD UGRASENA.

AND MATTERS STOOD THERE

*KAMSA'S WIVES

4

AH, BALARAMA! MY MIND IS SET ON MARRYING HER. BUT HER FATHER IS A VASSAL OF JARASANDHA AND HER BROTHER, RUKMI, HIS STAUNCH ALLY.

BUT IT IS RUMOURED THAT BHEESHMAKA AND HIS WIFE SECRETL HOPE THAT YOU WILL WIN RUKMINI.

MEANWHILE, AT VIDARBHA, IN THE GARDEN OF BHEESMAKA'S PALACE, RUKMINI TOO WAS LOST IN DREAMS OF THE YADAVA HERO WHO HAD WON HER HEART.

EVEN THE MIGHTY EMPEROR WITH ALL HIS ALLIES HAS NOT BEEN ABLE TO VANQUISH HIM. HE AND ONLY HE SHALL BE MY LORD.

SUDDENLY SHE HEARD VOICES.

MY FATHER! RUKMI! THEY'RE COMING THIS WAY.

7

THEN WHOM DO YOU SUGGEST?

THE EMPEROR'S FAVOURITE AND MY FRIEND — SHISHUPALA, THE CROWN PRINCE OF CHEDI. HE IS ENAMOURED OF RUKMINI.

THAT JACKAL! NEVER! I SHALL NEVER MARRY HIM. O RUKMI, HOW COULD YOU SELL YOUR OWN SISTER TO WIN THE EMPEROR'S FAVOUR? DON'T AGREE, FATHER, PLEASE DON'T AGREE!

BUT BHEESHMAKA INVARIABLY PERMITTED HIS ELDEST SON TO MAKE ALL MAJOR DECISIONS, EVEN IF THEY DID NOT COINCIDE WITH HIS OWN WISHES. HE HEAVED A SIGH.

ALL RIGHT, RUKMI. DO AS YOU WILL.

THEN I SHALL SEND A FORMAL PROPOSAL TO CHEDI AND INVITE SHISHUPALA TO COME AND MARRY RUKMINI.

THEY WALKED AWAY, LITTLE KNOWING THAT RUKMINI HAD OVERHEARD EVERY WORD OF THEIR CONVERSATION.

SO THEY DON'T EVEN PLAN TO HOLD A SWAYAMWARA. TO WHOM SHALL I SPEAK? WHAT SHALL I DO?

SUDDENLY AN IDEA OCCURRED TO HER.

WHY NOT! WHY SHOULDN'T I? AFTER ALL MY PARENTS ARE FOR IT.

SHE WENT INTO THE PALACE AND SENT FOR SUNANDA—A BRAHMAN WHOM SHE TRUSTED AND WHO WAS DEVOTED TO HER. WHEN HE CAME—

WHY DO YOU LOOK SO PALE, MY LITTLE ONE? WHAT'S THE MATTER?

SHE TOLD HIM ABOUT THE CONVERSATION SHE HAD OVERHEARD. THEN—

O VENERABLE ONE, WOULD IT BE WRONG ON MY PART TO SEND A SECRET MESSAGE TO THE YADAVA HERO?

NO, LITTLE ONE, NEVER. IT WOULD BE WRONG TO MARRY SHISHU-PALA WHEN YOUR HEART IS SET ON ANOTHER AND YOUR PARENTS HAVE IN THEIR HEARTS APPROVED.

BUT WITH WHOM CAN I ENTRUST SUCH A MESSAGE?

I WILL GO TO DWARAKA, RUKMINI. I SHALL CARRY THE MESSAGE FOR YOU.

RUKMINI WROTE OUT THE MESSAGE AND...

...GAVE IT TO THE BRAHMAN, TELLING HIM WHAT HER PLANS WERE.

...AND BE SURE TO TELL HIM THAT I WOULD NOT WANT MY KITH AND KIN TO BE KILLED ON MY ACCOUNT.

DO NOT WORRY, RUKMINI. I WILL NOT FORGET.

WITH GREAT DIFFICULTY, SUNANDA REACHED DWARAKA WHERE HE WAS GIVEN A WARM WELCOME. AFTER HE WAS RESTED AND REFRESHED—

O VENERABLE ONE, IF IT WOULD NOT MEAN BETRAYING ANY CONFIDENCE, TELL US WHY YOU HAVE COME TO OUR INACCESSIBLE CITY?

I HAVE COME WITH A MESSAGE FROM RUKMINI, THE PRINCESS OF VIDARBHA.

RUKMINI! MY OWN RUKMINI!

SUNANDA TOLD KRISHNA ABOUT THE CONVERSATION THAT RUKMINI HAD OVERHEARD. THEN HE GAVE KRISHNA, RUKMINI'S MESSAGE.

...I HAVE CHOSEN YOU AS MY HUSBAND. COME TO VIDARBHA, VANQUISH THE ARMIES OF JARASANDHA AND SHISHUPALA AND CLAIM ME...

WHEN KRISHNA FINISHED READING THE MESSAGE—

IF YOU DO NOT COME AND TAKE HER AWAY SHE HAS DECIDED TO GIVE UP HER LIFE.

SHE MENTIONS THAT IN THE MESSAGE. BUT LITTLE DOES SHE REALISE THAT I TOO HAVE SET MY HEART ON WINNING HER.

11

YES! I HAVE. BUT I KNOW THAT RUKMI DOES NOT WANT TO GIVE HER TO ME.

SUNANDA'S FACE FELL.

DOES THAT MEAN YOU WILL NOT...

NO. IT DOES NOT. NOW THAT SHE HAS REVEALED HER HEART TO ME, I SHALL MAKE HER MINE. I SHALL NOT HESITATE TO ROUT ALL THE KINGS WHO STAND IN MY WAY.

OVERJOYED, SUNANDA UNFOLDED THE REST OF RUKMINI'S PLANS. THEN—

THE GENTLE ONE IS ANXIOUS THAT THERE SHOULD BE NO FAMILY BLOOD SHED ON HER ACCOUNT.

IT IS BUT NATURAL FOR HER, A VERITABLE GODDESS,* TO FEEL THAT WAY.

* RUKMINI IS BELIEVED TO BE THE GODDESS LAXMI REBORN ON EARTH.

KRISHNA SENT FOR HIS CHARIOTEER. WHEN HE CAME—

GET MY CHARIOT READY AT ONCE, DARUKA. AND TELL BALARAMA THAT I SHALL BE LEAVING FOR VIDARBHA IMMEDIATELY.

MEANWHILE, RUKMI'S FORMAL PROPOSAL AND INVITATION HAD REACHED SHISHUPALA. HE WAS JUBILANT.

RUKMI SAYS THAT THERE IS NOT GOING TO BE ANY SWAYAMWARA. ALL I HAVE TO DO IS TO GO TO VIDARBHA AND MARRY RUKMINI. THE EMPEROR MUST HEAR THE GOOD NEWS.

BUT JARASANDHA WAS NOT AS CONFIDENT.

IT'S NOT AS EASY AS YOU THINK. I DO NOT TRUST THAT VILE COWHERD. HE IS SURE TO HEAR OF THE NEWS AND SNATCH THE BRIDE AWAY. WE WILL HAVE TO BE PREPARED.

JARASANDHA SENT FOR ALL HIS VASSALS AND ALLIES.

I AM BENT ON SECURING THE PRINCESS OF VIDARBHA FOR SHISHUPALA. YOU MUST BE READY TO CONFRONT THE COWHERD IF HE COMES THERE AND TRIES TO TAKE AWAY THE BRIDE.

MEANWHILE, AS SOON AS KRISHNA HAD LEFT DWARAKA, ONE OF BALARAMA'S SPIES CAME TO HIM.

LORD, THE EMPEROR HAS INFORMED ALL HIS ALLIES TO MARCH TO VIDARBHA. HE EXPECTS TROUBLE FROM US.

AND KRISHNA HAS GONE ALL ALONE!

GET MY CHARIOT READY! RALLY OUR ARMIES! ELEPHANTS, HORSES, CHARIOTS, ALL!

AT VIDARBHA, RUKMINI'S ANXIETY, INCREASED WITH EACH PASSING MOMENT.

THE HOUR IS DRAWING NEARER. WHY HAS MY LORD NOT YET COME?

DID MY MESSAGE DISGUST HIM? IF SO, THEN WHY HASN'T SUNANDA RETURNED?

HAVE A MANSION READY FOR HIM. FURNISH IT WITH EVERY LUXURY. I SHALL RIDE OUT TO RECEIVE HIM.

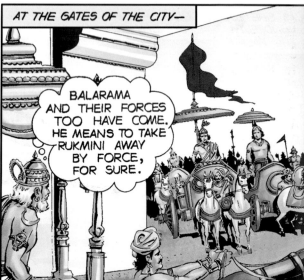

AT THE GATES OF THE CITY—

BALARAMA AND THEIR FORCES TOO HAVE COME. HE MEANS TO TAKE RUKMINI AWAY BY FORCE, FOR SURE.

WELCOME, O PRINCES! WE ARE HAPPY TO SEE YOU HERE. COME LET ME LEAD YOU TO THE PALACE WHERE YOU WILL STAY.

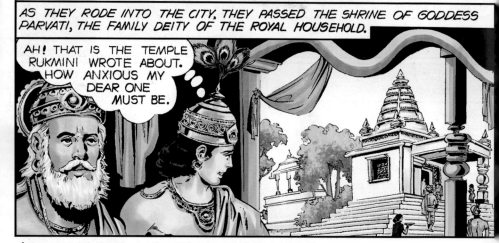

AS THEY RODE INTO THE CITY, THEY PASSED THE SHRINE OF GODDESS PARVATI, THE FAMILY DEITY OF THE ROYAL HOUSEHOLD.

AH! THAT IS THE TEMPLE RUKMINI WROTE ABOUT. HOW ANXIOUS MY DEAR ONE MUST BE.

*IN THOSE DAYS, A KSHATRIYA COULD CARRY AWAY HIS BRIDE, ESPECIALLY IF SHE SO DESIRED.

16

BALARAMA WAS CONCERNED ABOUT OTHER THINGS. HE TURNED TO BHEESHMAKA.

THE EMPEROR AND HIS MEN HAVE FLOODED THE CITY.

SHISHUPALA IS THE EMPEROR'S FAVOURITE. AND THE EMPEROR HAS MANY ALLIES.

THIS SHOULD HELP YOU PLAN YOUR STRATEGY.

MEANWHILE AT THE PALACE—

RUKMINI, YOUR CHARIOT HAS ARRIVED. ARE YOU READY?

I AM. LET US LEAVE.

ACCOMPANIED BY HER MAIDS, RUKMINI LEFT FOR THE SHRINE.

WHEN THEY REACHED THE GATES OF THE TEMPLE COURTYARD, SHE STEPPED OUT OF HER CHARIOT.

I DO NOT SEE KRISHNA AMONG THEM. THEY SAY HE IS DARK, WEARS A YELLOW ROBE, AND SPORTS A PEACOCK FEATHER IN HIS CROWN.

AS SHE WALKED TO THE TEMPLE, A MYRIAD EYES FOLLOWED HER EVERY MOVEMENT, DRINKING IN HER BEAUTY.

ALAS! SHE CAN NEVER BE MINE.

SHISHUPALA IS LUCKY. SHE IS THE VERY GODDESS OF WEALTH* INCARNATE.

* LAXMI

INSIDE THE TEMPLE—

I WORSHIP THEE, O FAITHFUL CONSORT OF SHIVA. I BOW TO THEE, THY LORD AND THY TWO SONS, GANESHA AND KARTIKEYA.

SHE WASHED THE GODDESS' FEET AND···

···PLACED OFFERINGS BEFORE HER.

THEN, OVERCOME BY THE THOUGHT THAT FILLED HER BEING, SHE PLEADED WITH THE GODDESS.

O GODDESS, PLEASE LET KRISHNA AND ONLY KRISHNA WIN AND WED ME.

HER WORSHIP OVER, SHE CAME OUT OF THE TEMPLE.

O GODDESS, DO NOT FAIL ME.

AS SHE WALKED TOWARDS THE GATE, HER EYES ANXIOUSLY SCANNED THE ASSEMBLY OF KINGS.

I DO NOT SEE HIM ANYWHERE.

HEAVY WAS HER HEART AND SLOW HER GAIT. THE CHARIOT LOOMED BEFORE HER ALL TOO SOON.

WILL KRISHNA EVER BECOME...

...MINE?

RUKMINI. IT'S ME. YOUR KRISHNA.

AND THE NEXT MOMENT SHE WAS SEATED NEXT TO HIM IN HIS CHARIOT.

STOP HIM!

RUKMINI! WAIT!

BUT KRISHNA'S CHARIOT SPED AWAY BLOWING DUST INTO THE EYES OF THE BEMUSED KINGS.

JARASANDHA WAS FURIOUS.

WHERE IS YOUR KSHATRIYA VALOUR? WHY DO YOU STAND THERE, AS IF YOU'VE LOST YOUR SENSES. PURSUE THEM!

JERKED INTO ACTION, THE KINGS CHARGED FORWARD.

BALARAMA TURNED TO KRISHNA.

THEY'RE GIVING CHASE. YOU RIDE ON. WE'LL FALL BACK AND DEAL WITH THEM.

WHEN RUKMINI LOOKED UP IN TERROR AT KRISHNA, HE LAUGHED HEARTILY AND ALLAYED HER FEARS.

DON'T BE ALARMED. OUR ARMIES WILL SOON ROUT THE ENEMY. BALARAMA WILL NOT LOSE HIS DEAR SISTER-IN-LAW SO EASILY.

HE WAS RIGHT.

CHASE THE JACKALS AWAY, MY MEN! SHOOT THEIR HORSES! DESTROY THEIR CHARIOTS!

WHILE BALARAMA WAS BUSY TACKLING JARASANDHA, SHISHUPALA AND THEIR HORDES, RUKMI CHARGED AHEAD AFTER KRISHNA'S VANISHING CHARIOT.

I WILL NOT RE-ENTER THE CAPITAL WITHOUT RUKMINI.

BALARAMA DID NOT TRY TO STOP HIM.

KRISHNA CAN DEAL WITH HIM, EVEN WITH RUKMINI IN HIS CHARIOT.

BALARAMA'S ONSLAUGHT WAS FIERCE.

LET US RE-TREAT, SHISHUPALA. THERE IS NO HOPE LEFT. THE COWHERDS ARE DETERMINED, RUKMINI IS LOST TO YOU.

ALAS! I FEEL AS IF MY WEDDED WIFE HAS BEEN ABDUCTED. SO SURE WAS I THAT SHE WAS MINE ALONE.

JARASANDHA TRIED TO CONSOLE HIM.

DON'T GRIEVE, SHISHUPALA. FORTUNE FAVOURED THEM AND THEY WON. WE SHALL CERTAINLY DEFEAT THEM WHEN OUR LUCK TURNS.

FULL OF HATRED FOR THE MAN WHO HAD WORSTED THEM, THE DISAPPOINTED SUITOR AND HIS WELL-WISHERS RETURNED TO THEIR CAPITALS.

MEANWHILE, RUKMI HAD ALMOST CAUGHT UP WITH KRISHNA.

TODAY I SHALL HUMBLE THE PRIDE OF THAT COWHERD WHO DARED ABDUCT MY SISTER.

SOON HIS CHARIOT WAS BUT A FEW FEET AWAY FROM KRISHNA.

FASTER... FASTER... FASTER...

STOP! STOP! WAIT, YOU DISGRACE TO THE RACE OF YADU! HOW DARE YOU KIDNAP MY SISTER, EVEN AS A CROW STEALS A SACRED OFFERING!

YOU WILY RASCAL. YOU HAVE PROVED YOUR CUNNING, NOW PROVE YOUR VALOUR.

RUKMI'S ARROW DID NOT EVEN MAKE A DENT IN KRISHNA'S ARMOUR.

KRISHNA PULLED OUT AN ARROW AND···

···LIFTED HIS BOW.

HE FIRST KILLED RUKMI'S HORSES AND···

···THEN SHATTERED HIS CHARIOT.

27

···AND RUSHED TOWARDS KRISHNA.

THE NEXT MOMENT, HOWEVER FOUND HIM HOLDING BUT THE HILT.

AS HE THREW IT AWAY IN DISGUST, KRISHNA PICKED UP HIS SWORD AND···

···WAS ABOUT TO RUSH TOWARDS HIM WHEN—

O VIRTUOUS LORD, PLEASE SPARE MY BROTHER. PLEASE DON'T KILL HIM.

ARISE, RUKMINI. FOR YOUR SAKE, RUKMI SHALL LIVE.

HE WENT UP TO RUKMI AND BOUND HIM WITH HIS OWN PRAPATA.*

I SHALL SHAVE OFF HALF HIS HAIR AND HALF HIS MOUSTACHE WITH THE BLADE OF MY SWORD. THERE COULD BE NO GREATER PUNISHMENT FOR A WARRIOR.

BALARAMA WAS HORRIFIED.

KRISHNA! WHAT ARE YOU DOING?

* CUMMERBUND.

KRISHNA, YOU HAVE PERFORMED AN IMPIOUS ACT; AN ACT DETESTED BY OUR RACE. TO DO WHAT YOU HAVE DONE TO A RELATIVE IS WORSE THAN KILLING HIM.

THEN HE TURNED TO RUKMINI.

PLEASE DO NOT TAKE OFFENCE, DEAR SISTER. YOUR BROTHER UNFORTUNATELY HAS REAPED THE FRUIT OF HIS OWN ACTIONS.

YOU ARE FREE TO GO, RUKMI.

ALAS! HE HAS ONLY ADDED INSULT TO INJURY. IT WERE BETTER THAT THEY HAD KILLED ME.

AS THE HUMILIATED RUKMI SLOWLY WALKED AWAY—

BUT WHERE SHALL I GO? BOUND BY MY OWN VOW, I CANNOT RETURN TO MY CAPITAL. I WILL HAVE TO BUILD A NEW CITY FOR MYSELF.

COME INTO THE CHARIOT, RUKMINI. WE MUST HURRY TO DWARAKA AND HAVE OUR WEDDING SOLEMNISED BY RITUALS.

A FEW DAYS LATER AT DWARAKA, KRISHNA WAS MARRIED TO RUKMINI WITH GREAT POMP AND CEREMONY.

CELEBRATING

50 YEARS

AMAR CHITRA KATHA

It was in 1967 that the first Amar Chitra Katha comic rolled off the presses, changing story-telling for children across India forever.

Five decades and more than 400 books later, we are still sharing stories from India's rich heritage, primarily because of the love and support shown by readers like yourself.

SO, FROM US TO YOU, HERE'S A BIG

THANK YOU

KRISHNA

The route to your roots

KRISHNA

Throwing his aged father into prison, Kamsa occupied the throne of Mathura. Commanding a formidable army he thought he was unstoppable. The threat to his power came from an unexpected quarter œ from a cowherd boy who was rumoured to be his cousin Devaki's eighth child, Krishna. Moreover there was a divine prophecy that Kamsa would meet his end at the hands of the eighth child of Devaki.

Script	Illustrations	Editor
Anant Pai	Ram Waeerkar	Anant Pai

Cover illustration by: Yusuf Bangalorewala

KRISHNA

VASUDEVA, A NOBLEMAN, HAD MARRIED PRINCESS DEVAKI OF MATHURA. HE WAS TAKING HIS BRIDE HOME.

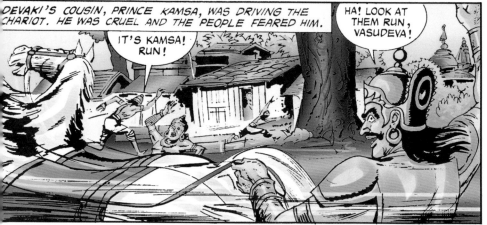

DEVAKI'S COUSIN, PRINCE KAMSA, WAS DRIVING THE CHARIOT. HE WAS CRUEL AND THE PEOPLE FEARED HIM.

IT'S KAMSA! RUN!

HA! LOOK AT THEM RUN, VASUDEVA!

JUST THEN A HEAVENLY VOICE WAS HEARD.

KAMSA, YOU SHALL SOON DIE. THE EIGHTH CHILD BORN TO DEVAKI WILL SLAY YOU!

IF SHE LIVES TO HAVE THAT EIGHTH CHILD! I'LL SLAY HER BEFORE, THEN!

KAMSA, DON'T!

YOUR SISTER HAS DONE YOU NO HARM, KAMSA. AS FOR THE CHILDREN WHO ARE YET TO BE BORN, I SHALL GIVE EACH ONE TO YOU, THE MOMENT IT IS BORN. I PROMISE.

I'LL SPARE DEVAKI, BUT I'LL MAKE SURE THAT YOU KEEP YOUR WORD.

KAMSA CONFINED DEVAKI AND VASUDEVA IN A PALACE. HE VISITED THEM EVERY TIME A BABY WAS BORN.

DEVAKI, GIVE ME THE BABY.

NO!

STOP HIM, MY LORD!

I AM HELPLESS, DEVAKI!

THUS DID THE COUPLE LOSE SIX OF THEIR CHILDREN. WHEN THE SEVENTH ONE WAS ABOUT TO BE BORN—

FROM THAT TYRANT, KAMSA? WE WILL NEVER SUCCEED.

WE MUST TRY AND SAVE THIS CHILD, DEVAKI.

2

WHO WILL HELP US? WHO WILL DARE RAISE A FINGER AGAINST ONE WHO HAS IMPRISONED HIS OWN FATHER?

YES. KING UGRASENA'S PLIGHT IS NO BETTER THAN OURS.

BUT DON'T LOSE HEART. REMEMBER THE PROPHECY.

THE SEVENTH CHILD WAS MIRACULOUSLY CARRIED TO ROHINI, VASUDEVA'S SECOND WIFE, IN GOKUL.

AND KAMSA WAS TOLD THAT DEVAKI'S BABY WAS STILL-BORN.

GOOD. THE NEXT WILL BE THE EIGHTH ONE — THE SLAYER OF MIGHTY KAMSA. HA!

PRADYOTA, HAVE VASUDEVA AND DEVAKI PUT IN CHAINS.

3

AS THE MONTHS WENT BY, HOWEVER, KAMSA GREW RESTLESS. CHANURA, THE COURT WRESTLER SENSED THIS.

LORD, WHY DON'T YOU COME TO THE GYMNASIUM?

NO, CHANURA!

I'LL BE AT PEACE ONLY WHEN I'VE KILLED THE EIGHTH CHILD.

IT RAINED HEAVILY ON THE EIGHTH DAY OF THE WANING MOON OF SHRAVAN*.

LORD! I THINK THE TIME HAS COME.

THE EIGHTH CHILD!

IT WAS PAST MIDNIGHT WHEN THE CHILD WAS BORN.

WHAT A BEAUTIFUL BABY HE IS! AND HE KNOWS HE MUST NOT CRY!

*5TH MONTH OF THE HINDU CALENDAR. STARTS LATE JULY AND ENDS IN 3RD WEEK OF AUGUST.

LOOK! THE CHAINS HAVE FALLEN OFF.

HOW I LONG TO HOLD MY SON... BUT... THESE CHAINS...

SUDDENLY—

AND THE DOORS HAVE OPENED! IT'S A MIRACLE!

DEVAKI! QUICK! GIVE THE CHILD TO ME.

I'LL TAKE HIM TO OUR FRIEND, NANDA, IN GOKUL.

AND VASUDEVA WALKED PAST THE GUARDS WHO HAD FALLEN ASLEEP.

GOKUL WAS ON THE OPPOSITE BANK OF THE RIVER YAMUNA WHICH WAS THEN IN SPATE.

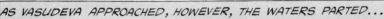

AS VASUDEVA APPROACHED, HOWEVER, THE WATERS PARTED...

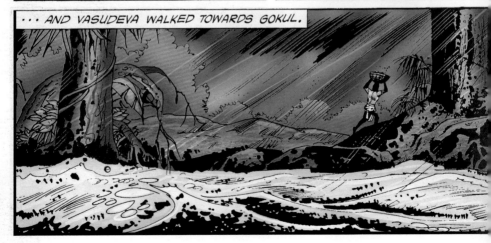

... AND VASUDEVA WALKED TOWARDS GOKUL.

AS HE NEARED GOKUL —

AH! THE CRY OF A NEW-BORN BABY. IT COMES FROM NANDA'S HOUSE.

NANDA'S WIFE YASHODA HAS HAD A CHILD.

IT'S A GIRL!

AND SURELY KAMSA WOULD NOT KILL A BABY GIRL.

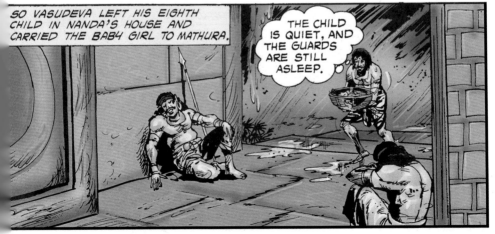

SO VASUDEVA LEFT HIS EIGHTH CHILD IN NANDA'S HOUSE AND CARRIED THE BABY GIRL TO MATHURA.

THE CHILD IS QUIET, AND THE GUARDS ARE STILL ASLEEP.

AS SOON AS VASUDEVA ENTERED THE PALACE, THE DOORS CLOSED. MINUTES LATER—

DID YOU HEAR THAT? IT'S THE WAIL OF A NEW-BORN BABY!

OOAH! OOAH!

COME! LET'S REPORT THIS TO THE KING!

THE EIGHTH CHILD! I WILL BE THERE IN A MOMENT.

WHEN KAMSA REACHED THE PALACE—

SPARE THE BABY, KAMSA. WHAT HARM CAN A GIRL DO YOU?

IGNORING HIM, KAMSA SEIZED THE BABY BY ITS LEGS AND WAS ABOUT TO DASH IT TO THE GROUND WHEN...

...IT ESCAPED FROM HIS GRIP AND FLEW TOWARDS THE SKY.

THEN—

THE ONE WHO SHALL DESTROY YOU STILL LIVES!

8

THE NEXT DAY, IN GOKUL—

THEY SAY THAT NANDA'S SON IS VERY BEAUTIFUL.

YES. AND HE HAS A BEAUTIFUL, NAME TOO— KRISHNA!

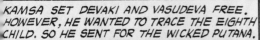

KAMSA SET DEVAKI AND VASUDEVA FREE. HOWEVER, HE WANTED TO TRACE THE EIGHTH CHILD. SO HE SENT FOR THE WICKED PUTANA.

PUTANA! GO OUT AND KILL EVERY CHILD BORN IN THE MONTH OF SHRAVAN!

PUTANA WENT ABOUT HER EVIL TASK.

I'LL SMEAR MY BREASTS WITH POISON AND FEED THE BABIES.

WHAT A SWEET BABY! MAY I HOLD IT?

THE MOTHER WAS FLATTERED. SHE GAVE THE BABY TO PUTANA.

A FEW MINUTES LATER—

MY BABY! WHAT'S HAPPENED TO MY BABY? AND WHERE IS PUTANA?

9

PUTANA HAD MADE HER WAY TO GOKUL!

WHO IS THAT BOY? WHEN WAS HE BORN?

HE IS KRISHNA, THE SON OF NANDA. HE WAS BORN IN THE MONTH OF SHRAVAN.

WHEN PUTANA FOUND KRISHNA ALONE —

LATER —

WHERE IS KRISHNA? I HAD LEFT HIM HERE!

OH! HE IS SAFE. BUT... WHO IS THIS WOMAN? WHY IS SHE LYING HERE?

I SAW HER NURSIN KRISHN

THEN SHE MUST BE PUTANA! PUTANA THE BABY-KILLER. SHE HAS KILLED MANY BABIES IN MATHURA.

SHE IS DEAD! THE EVIL PUTANA IS DEAD!

KRISHNA WAS SAFE, AND LIFE IN GOKUL WENT ON AS BEFORE

AS THE YEARS WENT BY, KRISHNA GREW TO BE AN ADORABLE LITTLE BOY.

KRISHNA! COME. I HAVE SOME FRESH BUTTER FOR YOU.

MAY I HAVE SOME MORE, MOTHER?

NO, KRISHNA. THAT'S ENOUGH FOR TODAY.

HERE'S BALARAMA*! GO AND PLAY WITH HIM.

THE TWO BOYS RAN OUT TO MEET THEIR FRIENDS.

KRISHNA, LET'S GO AND PLAY ON THE BANK OF THE YAMUNA.

WAIT. I'LL JOIN YOU IN A MINUTE.

DEVAKI'S SEVENTH CHILD, LOOKED AFTER BY ROHINI

KRISHNA TIPTOED INTO A NEARBY HOUSE...

...AND WENT STRAIGHT TO THE POTS OF BUTTER. SUDDENLY—

YOU NAUGHTY BOY! WHAT HAVE YOU DONE?

SHE DRAGGED KRISHNA TO YASHODA.

KRISHNA HAS EATEN ALL THE BUTTER IN MY HOUSE.

MY KRISHNA DID THAT? I DON'T BELIEVE IT. WHY, I GAVE HIM A WHOLE POT OF BUTTER ONLY A SHORT WHILE AGO.

BUT...

SISTER, YOU MUST KEEP THE MILK AND BUTTER BEYOND THE REACH OF CHILDREN.

THE GOPIKAS, AS THE WOMEN OF GOKUL WERE CALLED, TOOK YASHODA'S ADVICE. BUT KRISHNA WAS TOO CLEVER FOR THEM.

WHAT SHALL WE DO?

I HAVE AN IDEA.

SUCH WERE THE PRANKS KRISHNA PLAYED AND YASHODA FOUND IT DIFFICULT TO HANDLE THE COMPLAINTS THAT POURED IN.

YASHODA! KRISHNA WAS DRINKING THE MILK STRAIGHT FROM MY COW!

BUT MOTHER, THE COW GAVE IT TO ME.

AND THE BUTTER ON YOUR FACE? WHO GAVE THAT TO YOU?

THE GWALA BOYS SMEARED IT ON MY FACE. ALL OUT OF SPITE.

LOOK, MOTHER! I AM SO SHORT. THE BUTTER POT IS KEPT SO HIGH. HOW COULD I REACH IT?

KRISHNA, YOU ARE BECOMING NAUGHTIER DAY BY DAY. I WILL HAVE TO PUNISH YOU!

SO SHE TIED KRISHNA TO A HEAVY MORTAR.

BALARAMA WILL UNTIE ME. I'LL GO TO HIM.

14

BUT WHILE HE WAS ON HIS WAY THE MORTAR WAS CAUGHT BETWEEN TWO TREES.

...THE TREES CRASHED TO THE GROUND.

HE PULLED WITH ALL HIS HIS MIGHT TILL...

AS THE NEWS SPREAD, A CROWD GATHERED AT THE SPOT.

THIS BOY IS A MARVEL!

HE UPROOTED THOSE TWO MIGHTY TREES!

THESE STRANGE HAPPENINGS FRIGHTENED THE PEOPLE. SO THEY DECIDED TO LEAVE GOKUL AND GO TO VRINDAVAN.

AT VRINDAVAN—

MOTHER, MAY I GO WITH THE OTHERS TO GRAZE THE CATTLE?

YOU MAY, IF YOU STAY BY BALARAMA'S SIDE.

IN THE EVENING—

KRISHNA, WE ARE TOO TIRED TO HERD THE CATTLE.

WELL, THEN, I'LL HERD THEM FROM HERE.

KRISHNA TOOK UP HIS FLUTE.

SUCH SWEET MUSIC!

LOOK AT THE COWS!

THE GOPIKAS STOPPED THEIR CHORES TO LISTEN TO THE MELODIOUS STRAINS OF KRISHNA'S FLUTE.

HIS MUSIC FILLS ME WITH A STRANGE YEARNING.

ONE DAY —

IT'S HASTIN! RUN, KRISHNA!

I WON'T. I'LL TAME HIM.

PLEASE COME BACK, KRISHNA! HE'LL HURT YOU.

AS KRISHNA NEARED HIM, THE BULL SNORTED FIERCELY AND CHARGED.

BUT KRISHNA WAS TOO QUICK FOR HIM.

QUIET, MY FRIEND. I WON'T HURT YOU.

THUS DID KRISHNA, FIRMLY BUT GENTLY CALM THE ANGRY BULL.

ONE DAY KRISHNA FOUND ONE OF HIS FRIENDS CRYING.

WHAT'S THE MATTER? WHY ARE YOU CRYING?

MY COWS ARE DEAD. THEY DRANK WATER FROM KALIYA'S POOL.

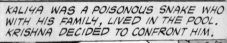

KRISHNA! KRISHNA! PLEASE COME BACK! KALIYA WILL KILL YOU!

BUT KRISHNA DIDN'T TURN BACK.

KRISHNA HAS DISAPPEARED. RUN AND TELL NANDA.

AS THE NEWS SPREAD, PEOPLE RUSHED TO THE POOL...

19

...ONLY TO FIND KRISHNA DANCING ON THE HOOD OF A MEEK KALIYA.

WHAT A BOY!

KRISHNA ORDERED KALIYA TO LEAVE THE POOL WITH HIS FAMILY. PEACE RETURNED TO VRINDAVAN.

ONE DAY, AS THE PEOPLE OF VRINDAVAN WERE PREPARING TO WORSHIP INDRA —

WE WORSHIP INDRA BECAUSE WE ARE AFRAID OF HIM WE OUGHT TO WORSHIP MOUNT GOVARDHANA WHOM WE LOVE!

KRISHNA IS RIGHT.

BUT WHILE GOVARDHANA WAS BEING WORSHIPPED, LOUD CLAPS OF THUNDER WERE HEARD...

...AND IT STARTED RAINING HEAVILY.

INDRA IS ANGRY. WE SHOULDN'T HAVE WORSHIPPED GOVARDHANA.

WHEN NEWS OF KRISHNA'S DEEDS REACHED MATHURA—

PRADYOTA! I HEAR THAT KRISHNA HELD THE MIGHTY GOVARDHANA ON HIS LITTLE FINGER.

SO THEY SAY, MY LORD!

YOU FOOL! WHY HAVE YOU LET HIM LIVE SO LONG? DIDN'T I ORDER YOU TO HAVE HIM KILLED SOMEHOW.

I HAVE TRIED EVERYTHING. EVEN THE MAD BULL, ARISHTA, AND THE WILD HORSE, KESHI.

KAMSA WAS SILENT FOR A WHILE. THEN—

HAVE IT ANNOUNCED THAT IN A FORTNIGHT I WILL PERFORM THE BOW SACRIFICE···

···AND···INVITE ALL, INCLUDING KRISHNA. YOU MUST SEE TO IT THAT HE DOES NOT RETURN ALIVE.

WHEN PRADYOTA LEFT, KAMSA SENT FOR CHANURA.

CHANURA! IF KRISHNA IS NOT KILLED BY PRADYOTA, CHALLENGE HIM TO A MATCH AND DON'T LET HIM ESCAPE ALIVE.

HE ALSO SUMMONED THE CHIEF OF MAHOUTS.

YOU WILL STAND AT THE ENTRANCE TO THE YAGNA HALL. WHEN KRISHNA COMES THERE SEE THAT YOUR ELEPHANT TRAMPLES HIM TO DEATH.

THEN HE SENT FOR THE WISE AKRURA.

I WANT THE WHOLE WORLD TO KNOW OF KRISHNA. ASK HIM TO COME TO MATHURA, FOR THE BOW SACRIFICE.

AKRURA SET OUT ON HIS MISSION.

AT VRINDAVAN—

YOU MUST PERMIT KRISHNA TO COME TO MATHURA.

NO, AKRURA I DON'T TRUST KAMSA. I WILL NOT SEND MY SON.

WHEN AKRURA SAW THAT NANDA WAS ADAMANT, HE TOLD HIM THE TRUTH ABOUT KRISHNA.

NANDA! KRISHNA IS THE SON OF PRINCE VASUDEVA.

I DON'T BELIEVE IT.

SO AKRURA NARRATED THE STORY OF KRISHNA'S BIRTH AND HOW HE WAS BROUGHT TO GOKUL.

KRISHNA, DID YOU HEAR THAT? AKRURA SAYS THAT DEVAKI IS YOUR MOTHER. I AM YOUR MOTHER, AREN'T I?

PLEASE DON'T BE UPSET, MOTHER. I SHALL ALWAYS LOOK UPON YOU AS MY MOTHER. BUT...

...I SEEK THE PERMISSION OF MY ELDERS TO GO TO MATHURA!

VERY GOOD, MY BOY! THE YADAVA CHIEFS WILL SEE THAT NO HARM COMES TO YOU.

YOU MAY GO, MY SON BUT BEWARE OF KAMSA!

THE NEXT MORNING, KRISHNA, ACCOMPANIED BY BALARAMA, LEFT FOR MATHURA.

TAKE CARE OF YOURSELVES, CHILDREN.

AND COME BACK SOON.

AS THEY NEARED THE CITY OF MATHURA, KRISHNA DECIDED TO WALK. SUDDENLY—

RISE, O WOMAN! WHY DO YOU FALL AT MY FEET?

LOOK AT TRIVAKRA! HER HUMPED BACK HAS STRAIGHTENED OUT.

A MIRACLE! HE MUST BE OUR SAVIOUR.

THE NEWS SPREAD AND A CROWD FOLLOWED KRISHNA AND BALARAMA TO THE GATE OF THE YAGNA HALL.

SIR, I AM KRISHNA. MAY I INSPECT THE BOW?

CERTAINLY! DO STEP IN.

IT WAS PRADYOTA.

SO THIS IS THE BOY I HAVE TO KILL.

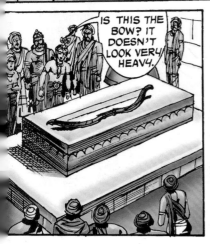

IS THIS THE BOW? IT DOESN'T LOOK VERY HEAVY.

BUT IT IS! EVEN THE MIGHTY WRESTLER CHANURA CANNOT LIFT IT.

I STILL DON'T BELIEVE IT IS THAT HEAVY.

KRISHNA LIFTED THE BOW...

...AND BROKE IT.

THE JUBILANT CROWD RUSHED INTO THE SACRIFICIAL HALL.

VICTORY TO KRISHNA! HE IS THE SAVIOUR!

WHEN PRADYOTA WENT TO KAMSA WITH THE NEWS—

KRISHNA BROKE THE BOW AND YOU STOOD AND WATCHED HIM DO IT!

YOU HAD ORDERS TO KILL HIM, HADN'T YOU?

I KNOW, MY LORD! BUT THE CROWD THAT FOLLOWED HIM WAS FRIGHTENING.

THE NEXT MORNING AS KRISHNA APPROACHED THE GATE OF THE YAGNA HALL—

WATCH OUT, KRISHNA! THE ELEPHANT...!

THE ELEPHANT SEIZED KRISHNA.

BUT KRISHNA ESCAPED ITS GRIP, LIFTED IT BY ITS TRUNK...

...AND HURLING IT INTO THE AIR...

...KILLED IT.

THEN WITH *BALARAMA*, HE TOOK HIS PLACE IN THE ARENA WHERE THE GAMES WERE BEING HELD.

KRISHNA, KAMSA HAS HEARD MUCH ABOUT YOUR STRENGTH AND VALOUR. HE HAS INVITED YOU TO WRESTLE... WITH ME!

IT'S A HONOUR CHANURA. I AM READY.

FIRST MUSHTIKA WILL WRESTLE WITH YOUR BROTHER.

BALARAMA AND MUSHTIKA FACED EACH OTHER.

IT IS UNFAIR OF KAMSA TO PIT THIS BOY AGAINST MUSHTIKA! HE'LL BE KILLED.

BUT THE CROWD WAS IN FOR A SURPRISE.

LOOK! MUSHTIKA IS IN TROUBLE!

IT WAS BALARAMA WHO KILLED MUSHTIKA.

28

NOW CHANURA STEPPED FORWARD.

ARE YOU READY, KRISHNA?

CHANURA TRIED TO CRUSH KRISHNA IN HIS MIGHTY ARMS. BUT KRISHNA SLIPPED AWAY.

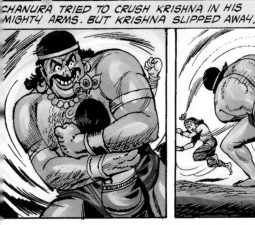

DISAPPOINTED, CHANURA RUSHED MADLY AT HIM.

BUT KRISHNA NIMBLY STEPPED ASIDE AND PICKING HIM UP...

...DASHED HIM TO THE GROUND.

CHANURA IS DEAD!

VICTORY TO KRISHNA!

THUD

CRASH

AS KAMSA'S SOLDIERS MOVED TOWARDS THE YADAVA CHIEFS...

···KRISHNA RUSHED TOWARDS KAMSA···

···TOOK AWAY HIS SWORD···

···AND THROWING HIM TO THE GROUND, KILLED HIM.

THE CROWD WAS STUNNED INTO SILENCE. KRISHNA LIFTED THE CROWN FROM KAMSA'S HEAD···

··AND BEGAN WALKING TOWARDS ·HE PALACE.

HE WALKED PAST THE GUARDS···

·· AND WENT UP TO ·GRASENA, KAMSA'S FATHER.

MY LORD!

KRISHNA!

MY LORD! I HAVE BROUGHT YOU WHAT RIGHTFULLY BELONGS TO YOU.

THIS WAS ONLY THE BEGINNING. KRISHNA LIVED LONG TO TRIUMPH OVER ALL EVIL. HIS GREAT DEEDS ARE REMEMBERED TO THIS DAY.

Amar Chitra Katha's

EPICS & MYTHOLOGY

BRAVEHEARTS

VISIONARIES

FABLES & HUMOUR

INDIAN CLASSICS

CONTEMPORARY CLASSICS

EXCITING STORY CATEGORIES,
ONE AMAZING DESTINATION.

From the episodes of Mahabharata to the wit of Birbal,
from the valour of Shivaji to the teachings of Tagore,
from the adventures of Pratapan to the tales of Ruskin Bond –
Amar Chitra Katha stories span across different genres to get you the best of literatur

THE SYAMANTAKA GEM

The route to your roots

THE
SYAMANTAKA GEM

To the women of Dwarka, Krishna is the most coveted jewel, the husband they yearn for. For most of the men, the Syamantaka, the sun-god's shining gem, is the most sought-after prize. This is hardly surprising – it is known to regularly bestow a hoard of solid gold on their Prince Satrajit. When the gem goes missing, suspicion falls on Krishna. He must prove his innocence, but danger and upheaval threaten at every turn.

Script	Illustrations	Editor
Kamala Chandrakant	H.S.Chavan	Anant Pai

Cover illustration by: M.N.Nangare

THE SYAMANTAKA GEM

PRINCE SATRAJIT OF DWARAKA WAS A
DEVOTEE OF SURYA, THE SUN GOD.

YOUR DEVOTION MERITS A GIFT. THE SYMANTAKA GEM IS YOURS. TAKE IT.

THE SUN GOD DISAPPEARED.

THE JEWEL SHINES SO BRIGHTLY THAT IT LIGHTS MY PATH.

SATRAJIT RODE BACK TO DWARAKA WEARING ABOUT HIM THE RADIANCE OF THE SYAMANTAKA.

WHAT HAS HAPPENED TO OUR PRINCE?

HE SHINES WITH A STRANGE LIGHT.

3

WONDERSTRUCK THEY WENT TO SHRI KRISHNA, THE ALL-KNOWING ONE.

LORD KRISHNA, BEHOLD! THE SUN HAS COME TO EARTH.

SURYA HAS GIVEN SATRAJIT THE SYAMANTAKA JEWEL.

THE JEWEL HAS THE POWER TO PREVENT FAMINE AND WAR.

MEANWHILE SATRAJIT REACHED HIS PALACE.

HAIL!

HAIL!

4

THAT NIGHT HE WENT TO BED, WEARING THE GEM.

THE NEXT MORNING—

GOLD COINS!

HE INSTALLED THE GEM IN A TEMPLE...

...AND WORSHIPPED IT.

IT GIVES FORTH EIGHT MEASURES OF GOLD A DAY!

THE GEM BROUGHT PEACE AND PROSPERITY IN ITS WAKE.

WE HAVE BEEN FAVOURED!

WE WILL NEVER KNOW FAMINE OR WAR!

ONE DAY KRISHNA VISITED SATRAJIT.

WELCOME, SHRI KRISHNA.

DWARAKA IS HUMMING WITH TALES OF YOUR GOOD FORTUNE

7

A FEW DAYS LATER, SATRAJIT'S BROTHER, PRASENA, WENT OUT ON A HUNT, WEARING THE JEWEL.

TAKE CARE, PRASENA.

I MAY LOSE MY LIFE BUT I'LL GUARD THE JEWEL.

WHEN HE REACHED THE FOREST, PRASENA DISMOUNTED AND WAITED FOR THE GAME.

AH... AT LAST.

A SNAKE!

WHAT A NARROW ESCAPE!

BUT—

AAAGH!

AS THE LION WALKED AWAY WITH THE GEM, JAMBAVAN, KING OF THE BEARS, SAW HIM.

WHAT A FINE JEWEL!

HE ATTACKED THE LION...

...AND KILLED IT.

I'LL GIVE IT TO MY SON.

HERE IS SOMETHING FOR YOU, SON!

MEANWHILE AT DWARAKA —

PRASENA HAS NOT RETURNED FROM THE HUNT.

WHAT COULD HAVE HAPPENED TO HIM?

I AM SURE, KRISHNA MUST HAVE KILLED MY BROTHER FOR THE SAKE OF THE GEM.

SATRAJIT SUSPECTS ME.

I MUST FIND THE JEWEL AND ESTABLISH MY INNOCENCE.

LOOK, GOLD COINS.

THE LION MUST HAVE SOMEHOW GOT HOLD OF THE SYAMANTAKA JEWEL.

AH! THERE LIES OUR CULPRIT.

I WONDER WHO TOOK THE GEM.

DEAD!

I WONDER WHO KILLED IT.

13

16

THE WINNER TAKES THE GEM.

THEY FIRST FOUGHT WITH WEAPONS.

THEN WITH STONES AND MOUNTAIN ROCKS...

...AND WHEN THOSE WERE EXHAUSTED, WITH UPROOTED TREES.

MEANWHILE, OUTSIDE THE CAVE—

IT IS TWELVE DAYS SINCE HE WENT IN THERE.

HE MUST BE DEAD.

HE ASKED US TO WAIT HERE.

I AM HUNGRY!

I AM TIRED.

LET'S GO HOME.

AN OWL HOOTED –

WHAT WAS THAT EERIE SOUND?

ONLY AN OWL.

LET'S GO AWAY.

OVERCOME BY FEAR AND EXHAUSTION, THEY LEFT.

MEANWHILE AT DWARAKA KRISHNA'S WIFE AND PARENTS WERE ANXIOUS.

THERE IS NO NEWS OF KRISHNA.

MY LORD, RETURN TO ME, SAFE AND SOUND.

LOOK! A CLOUD OF DUST.

KRISHNA?

BUT—

WE HAVE COME BACK WITHOUT KRISHNA.

WE FEAR HE IS DEAD.

KRISHNA WAS NOT DEAD. AFTER TWENTY EIGHT DAYS OF CONTINUOUS FIGHTING—

YOU ARE INVINCIBLE. I SURRENDER.

ALONG WITH THE GEM PLEASE ACCEPT...

NO SOONER HAD THEY GARLANDED EACH OTHER THAN JAMBAVATI TURNED INTO A BEAUTIFUL WOMAN.

KRISHNA RETURNED WITH HIS BRIDE AND THE SYAMANTAKA JEWEL TO DWARAKA.

KRISHNA HAS COME; WITH A LOVELY BRIDE.

TELL SATRAJIT TO COME TO THE COURT. I HAVE SOMETHING FOR HIM.

WHEN SATRAJIT CAME—

I HAVE FOUND THE SYAMANTAKA GEM.

AFTER KRISHNA HAD TOLD HIS STORY—

I DID YOU GRIEVOUS WRONG.

IT WAS OUT OF YOUR IGNORANCE.

SATRAJIT WANTED TO MAKE AMENDS.

KEEP THE JEWEL, KRISHNA...

...AND ALSO ACCEPT MY DAUGHTER, SATYABHAMA IN MARRIAGE.

I WILL MARRY YOUR DAUGHTER WITH PLEASURE. THE GEM IS RIGHTFULLY YOURS. KEEP IT. YOU MAY HOWEVER GIVE ME THE GOLD IT YIELDS.

MEANWHILE, SATYABHAMA'S DISAPPOINTED SUITORS, AKRURA, KRITAVARMA AND SHATADHANWA, NURSED THOUGHTS OF REVENGE.

SHATADHANWA, WE HAVE BEEN INSULTED.

YES, SATRAJIT HAD PROMISED HIS DAUGHTER TO ONE OF US. WHY DON'T YOU KILL HIM AND MAKE THE SYAMANTAKA JEWEL YOURS?

EAGER TO POSSESS THE GEM, THE EVIL SHATADHANWA DECIDED TO KILL SATRAJIT.

THE JEWEL WILL SOON BE MINE.

A..A..AH!

TAKING THE GEM...

...SHATADHANWA RODE AWAY.

THE WOMEN OF SATRAJIT'S HOUSE, SET UP LOUD LAMENTATIONS.

SATYABHAMA WAS HEART-BROKEN.

FATHER...
FATHER...

SHE WENT TO KRISHNA WHO WAS IN HASTINAPURA.

LORD, MY FATHER HAS BEEN SLAIN.

YOU MUST BE BRAVE.

MEANWHILE THE GUILTY SHATADHANWA APPEALED TO KRITAVARMA.

PLEASE, SHELTER ME FROM THE WRATH OF KRISHNA.

GO ELSEWHERE.

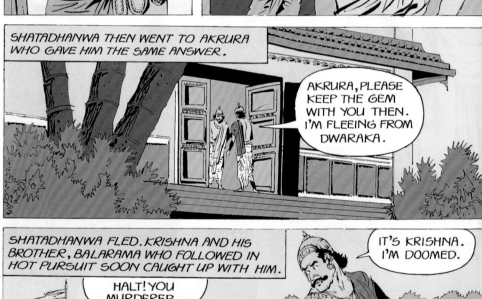

SHATADHANWA THEN WENT TO AKRURA WHO GAVE HIM THE SAME ANSWER.

AKRURA, PLEASE KEEP THE GEM WITH YOU THEN. I'M FLEEING FROM DWARAKA.

SHATADHANWA FLED. KRISHNA AND HIS BROTHER, BALARAMA WHO FOLLOWED IN HOT PURSUIT SOON CAUGHT UP WITH HIM.

HALT! YOU MURDERER.

IT'S KRISHNA. I'M DOOMED.

NEAR MITHILA, ONE OF SHATADHANWA'S HORSES TRIPPED...

...AND FELL.

SHATADHANWA FELL DEAD.

HE DOES NOT HAVE THE JEWEL. HE MUST HAVE GIVEN IT TO AKRURA.

WHEN KRITAVARMA LEARNT OF SHATADHANWA'S FATE—

KRISHNA HAS KILLED SHATADHANWA, I HEAR.

HE WILL COME HERE NEXT. LET US FLEE BEFORE HE GETS HERE.

A FEW DAYS LATER AT DWARAKA—

UNLESS THE GEM IS FOUND, I WILL REMAIN SUSPECT IN THE EYES OF THE PEOPLE. ONLY AKRURA CAN HELP ME. I WILL SEND FOR HIM.

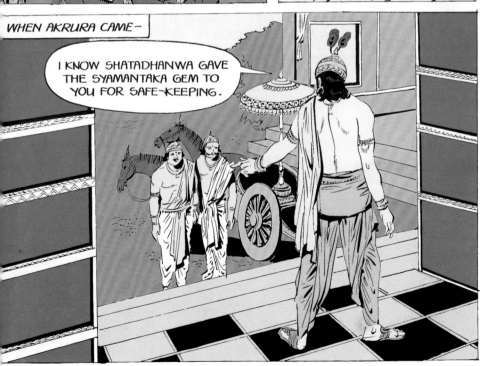

WHEN AKRURA CAME—

I KNOW SHATADHANWA GAVE THE SYAMANTAKA GEM TO YOU FOR SAFE-KEEPING.

AKRURA, YOU MAY KEEP THE GEM. BUT PLEASE ADMIT THAT YOU ARE IN POSSESSION OF IT. THIS WILL CLEAR ALL DOUBTS IN THE MIND OF THE PEOPLE.

HERE IS THE GEM. YOU MAY TAKE IT.

I WILL BE BACK AFTER SHOWING THE GEM TO THE PEOPLE OF DWARAKA.

KRISHNA IS A STRANGE PERSON.

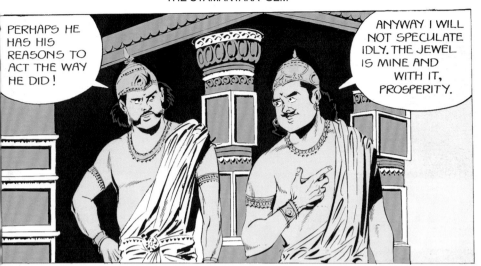

PERHAPS HE HAS HIS REASONS TO ACT THE WAY HE DID!

ANYWAY I WILL NOT SPECULATE IDLY. THE JEWEL IS MINE AND WITH IT, PROSPERITY.

HAVING SET THE MINDS OF THE CITIZENS AT REST KRISHNA TOO WAS ABLE TO RELAX IN THE COMPANY OF HIS MANY WIVES.